What Moms Can't Do

To Kathy and Joyce, Blanche and Irma:
My favorite moms—D.W.

For Jackie and Nana Juney—D. C.

ISBN 0-439-32698-2

Text copyright © 2001 by Douglas Wood.
Illustrations copyright © 2001 by Doug Cushman.
All rights reserved. Published by Scholastic Inc.,
557 Broadway, New York, NY 10012, by arrangement with
Simon & Schuster Books for Young Readers, an imprint of Simon & Schuster
Children's Publishing Division. SCHOLASTIC and associated logos
are trademarks and/or registered trademarks of Scholastic Inc.

12 11 10 9 8 7 6 5 4   2 3 4 5 6 7/0

Printed in the U.S.A.   08

First Scholastic printing, April 2002

Book design by Anahid Hamparian

The text of this book is set in 20-point Garamond Book.
The illustrations are rendered in pen and ink, watercolors
and gouache, and lots of coffee.

What Moms Can't Do

by **Douglas Wood**

pictures by **Doug Cushman**

SCHOLASTIC INC.

New York Toronto London Auckland Sydney
Mexico City New Delhi Hong Kong Buenos Aires

There are lots of things
that regular people can do
but moms can't.

Moms can't wait ...

to wake up kids in the morning.

They can't make the bed
without lots of help.

Moms can never pick out just the right clothes.

And they have trouble keeping things cleaned up.

Moms can't have Yummos with purple
marshmallows for breakfast. Only
coffee, or tea, or yogurt, or bran flakes.
Yuck.

They need a little advice when they're packing lunches.

Moms can't run very fast.

Sometimes moms can't hear themselves think (whatever that means).

Moms are not good at saying good-bye.

Even to the teacher.

Moms can't push grocery carts fast enough.

And sometimes they need help opening doors.

Moms don't know how to keep
salamanders in their shirts.

Or toads in their pockets.

Moms aren't very good tacklers.

And they can't make a basket on their own.

Moms are easy to squirt,
    but they have a hard time squirting you.

Usually.

Moms really don't like to watch movies by themselves.

And sometimes they need protection
during the scary parts.

They feel much better with someone
on their lap.

Moms can't let go of a hug without a kiss.
Or two.
Or nine.

There are lots of things moms can't do.
More than you can count.
But there's one thing they do better
than almost anyone . . .

and that's
love
you.